A Tune A Day

for Flute.
Selected and Arranged
by Martin Frith.

Popular Repertoire.

Wise Publications

London/New York/Sydney

Preface

The ten sections in this book each contain a selection of popular titles, which have been carefully arranged and graded.
They provide extra progressive practice material for students working through the corresponding
A Tune A Day instrumental tutors.
At the beginning of each section the stage which the student should have reached in A Tune A Day in order to cope with the material is
clearly stated. In many cases the range of notes expected to be known, the keys used and the general musical objectives of the
section are also outlined.
Some of the tunes have been very slightly modified to accommodate students' limited technical ability at various stages. 'Correct' rhythmic
notation has always been used, at variance with certain practices in A Tune A Day, where dotted notation and syncopation are often not
introduced until quite late in the course. Octave shifts sometimes occur for two reasons: in the earlier stages to take account of the
student's limited range, and in the later stages to provide added practice and interest.
Chord symbols are included to heighten the student's harmonic awareness, and to provide a basis for possible improvisation.

Exclusive Distributors:
Music Sales Limited
8/9 Frith Street, London W1V 5TZ.
Music Sales Pty Limited
120 Rothschild Avenue, Rosebery, NSW 2018, Australia.

This book © Copyright 1991 by
Wise Publications Order No. BM11296
ISBN 0.7119.2511.9

Designed by Pearce Marchbank Studio
Compiled & arranged by Martin Frith
Music processed by Bill Pitt Musical Services

SECTION 1 (LESSONS 1-6)

Range of notes learnt so far: *Keys used in this section:*

C Major   F Major

Objectives:

1. To play these familiar tunes.

2. The use of key signatures and ties.

LITTLE BROWN JUG

MY OLD MAN'S A DUSTMAN

J.P. Long, E. Mayne & A. Le Fre

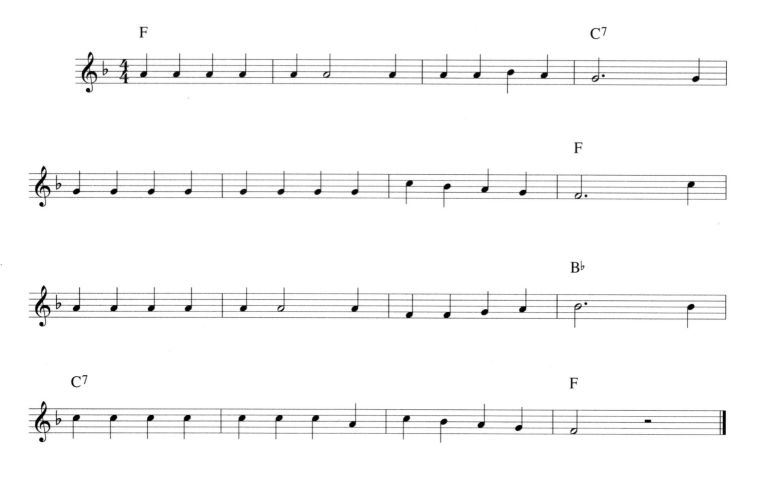

KUM BA YAH

Folk Song

SECTION 2 (LESSONS 7-12)

Range of notes:

Keys used:

A Minor   G Major

Objectives:

1. To extend your knowledge of the range.

2. To become familiar with quavers, slurs and ties.

EIGHT DAYS A WEEK

John Lennon & Paul McCartney

WHAT SHALL WE DO WITH THE DRUNKEN SAILOR?

MAYBE BABY

PEGGY SUE

Jerry Allison, Norman Petty & Buddy Holly

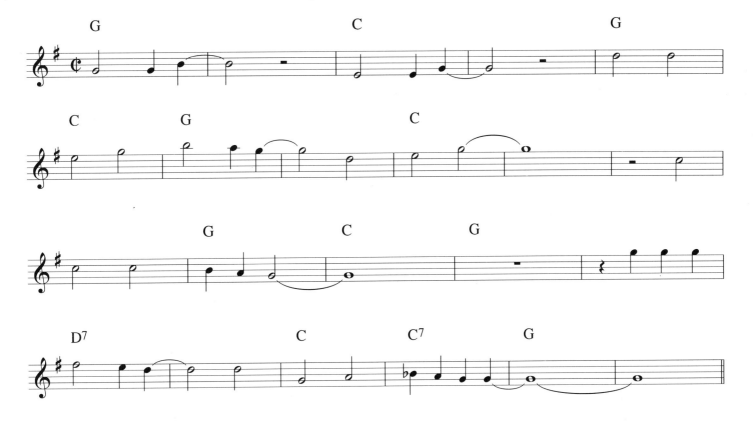

BE-BOP-A-LULA

Gene Vincent & Sheriff Tex Davis

SECTION 3 (LESSONS 13-17)

Range of notes:

Keys used:

   G Major   D Major   D Minor

Objectives:

1. Up beats and $\frac{3}{4}$ time.

2. New notes and dotted rhythms.

3. The use of repeats and 1st and 2nd time bars.

JAMBALAYA (ON THE BAYOU)

Hank Williams

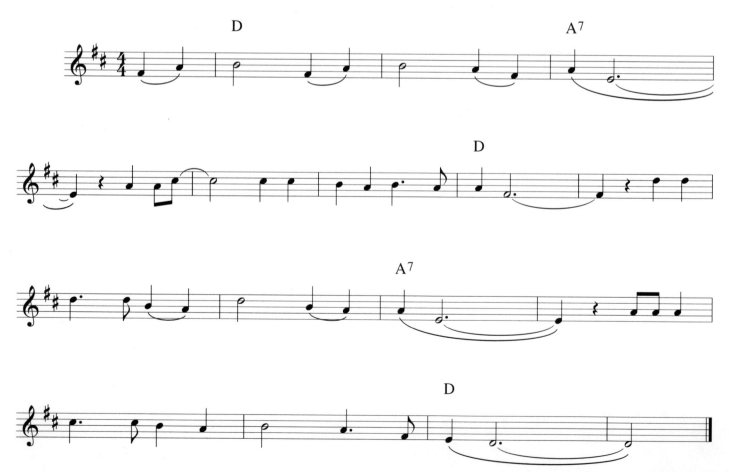

I DON'T KNOW HOW TO LOVE HIM

Andrew Lloyd Webber

SUNNY

Bobby Hebb

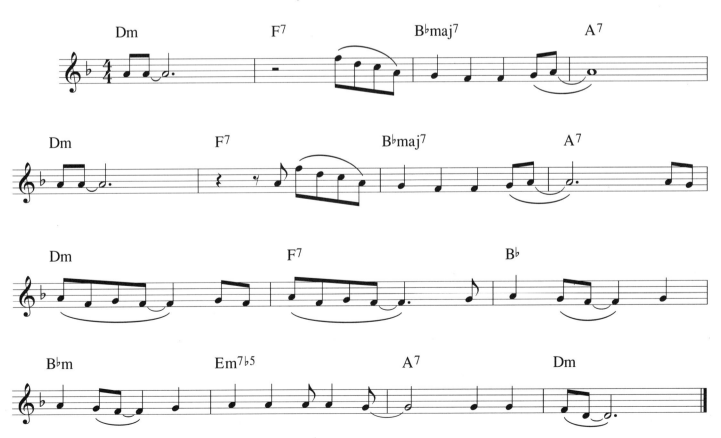

ON TOP OF OLD SMOKEY

Traditional
© Copyright 1991 Dorsey Brothers Music Limited, 8/9 Frith Street, London W1.
All Rights Reserved. International Copyright Secured.

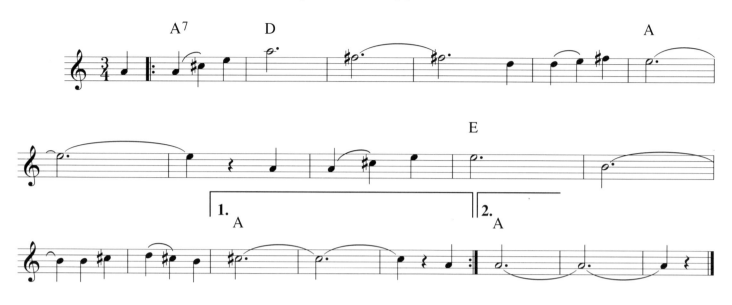

BILL BAILEY WON'T YOU PLEASE COME HOME

Traditional
© Copyright 1991 Dorsey Brothers Music Limited, 8/9 Frith Street, London W1.
All Rights Reserved. International Copyright Secured.

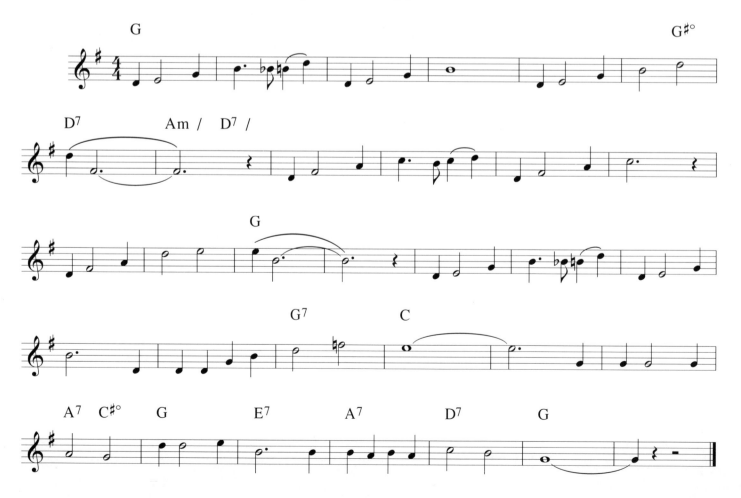

SECTION 4 (LESSONS 18-25)

Range of notes:

Keys used:

G Major   D Major   B♭ Major
                                            G Minor

Objectives:

1. *Introducing a new time signature:* $\frac{6}{8}$
2. *Introducing dynamics.*
3. *Change of key signature and time signature.*

DANCE OF THE CUCKOOS

T. Marvin Hatley

© Copyright 1930, 1932 Hatley Music Company, USA. Controlled throughout the Eastern Hemisphere by Robert Kingston (Music) Limited, 43 Fairfield Road, Uxbridge, Middlesex.

All Rights Reserved. International Copyright Secured.

Quickly

'ALLO, 'ALLO

David Croft & Roy Moore

DO THAT TO ME ONE MORE TIME

Toni Tennille

Easy Rock

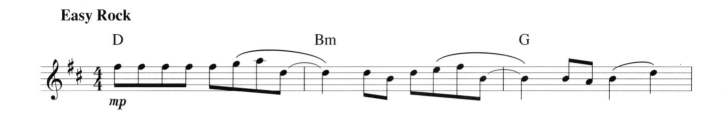

LOVE IS BLUE (L'AMOUR EST BLEU)

Andre Popp

Moderately

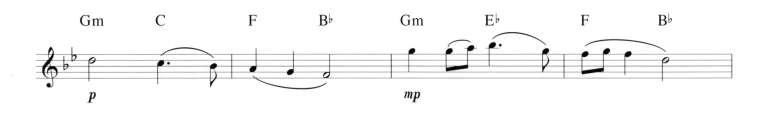

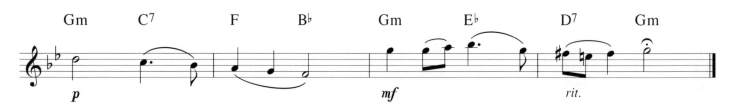

TAKE THAT LOOK OFF YOUR FACE

Andrew Lloyd Webber

Easy Rock

SECTION 5 (LESSONS 26-30)

Range of notes:

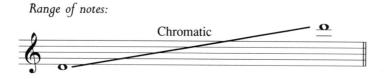

Chromatic

Keys used:

G Major   D Major   C Minor

Objectives:

1. Using longer slurs.

2. Introducing rhythms

SCARBOROUGH FAIR

Traditional

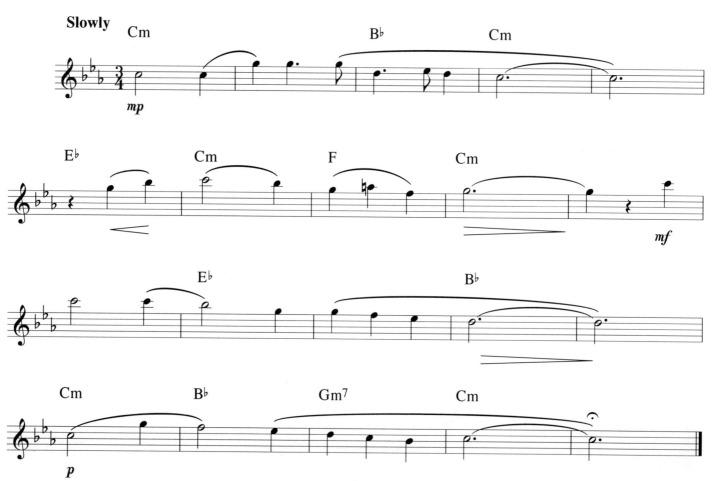

NEIGHBOURS

Tony Hatch & Jackie Trent

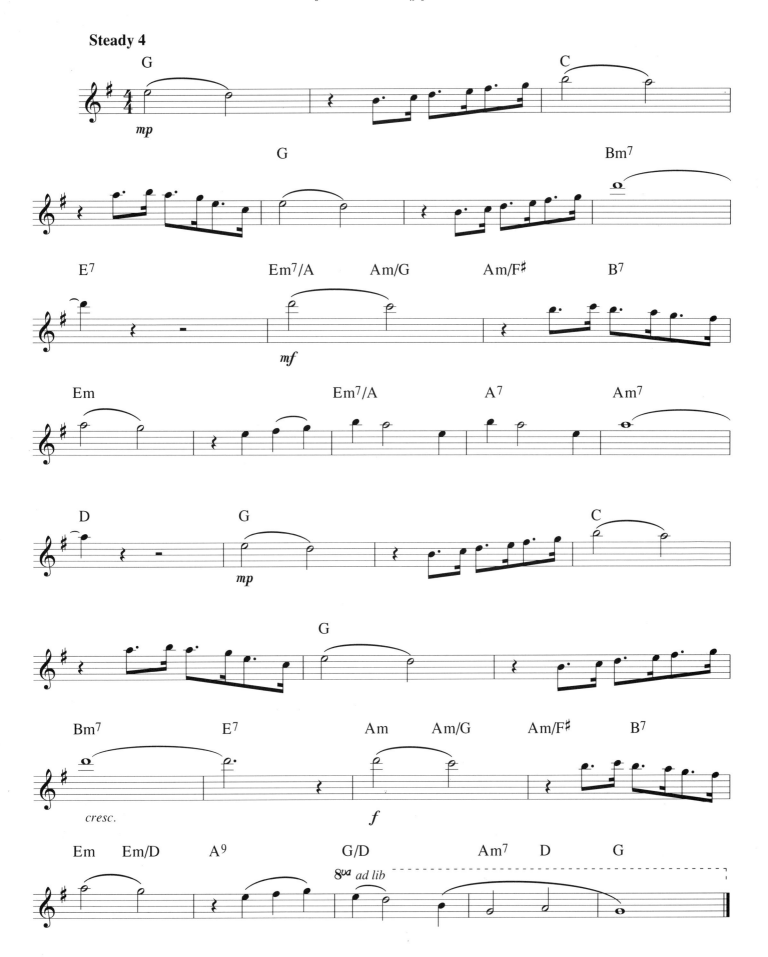

CHATTANOOGA CHOO CHOO

Harry Warren

SECTION 6 (LESSONS 31-33)

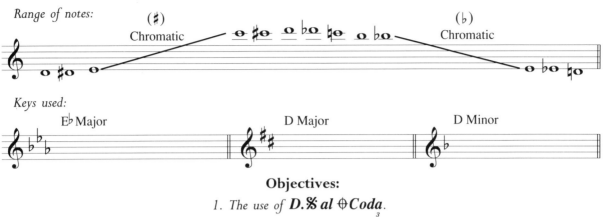

Objectives:

1. The use of *D.℀ al* ⊕ *Coda*.
2. Introducing triplet quavers.

MOONLIGHT SERENADE

Glenn Miller

WHEN I'M SIXTY-FOUR

John Lennon & Paul McCartney

Moderately

THE INCREDIBLE HULK (THEME FROM)

Joe Harnell

SECTION 7 (BOOK TWO, LESSONS 1-4)

Range of notes:

Objectives:

1. Extending the upper range.

2. Introducing more complex rhythmic patterns.

DOWNTOWN

Tony Hatch

© Copyright 1964 by ATV Music, under licence to EMI Songs Limited, 127 Charing Cross Road, London WC2 for the World.

All Rights Reserved. International Copyright Secured.

GOODBYE YELLOW BRICK ROAD

Elton John & Bernie Taupin

Moderately

SECTION 8 (BOOK TWO, LESSONS 5-8)

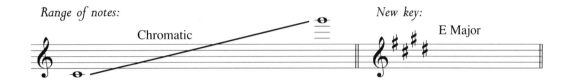

Range of notes: Chromatic *New key:* E Major

Objectives:

1. Further extending the range.

2. Introducing triplet crotchets

MICHELLE

John Lennon & Paul McCartney

© Copyright 1965 Northern Songs, under licence to EMI Songs Limited, 127 Charing Cross Road, London WC2.

All Rights Reserved. International Copyright Secured.

25

HAWAII FIVE-O

Mort Stevens

With a driving beat

Now try lines 1 & 2 up the octave like this:-

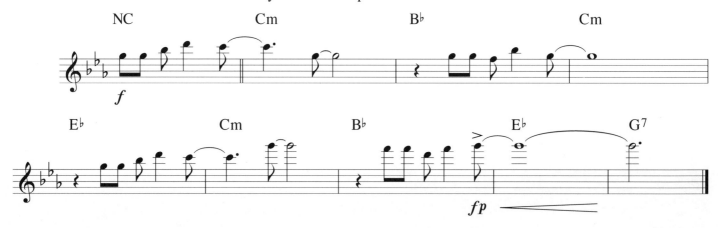

FERRY 'CROSS THE MERSEY

Gerard Marsden

Moderately quick

SECTION 9 (BOOK TWO, LESSONS 9-12)

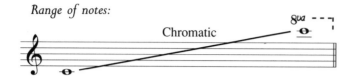

Range of notes:

Chromatic

Objectives:

1. Full use of range.

2. More triplet crotchets.

JUST THE WAY YOU ARE

Billy Joel

Moderately

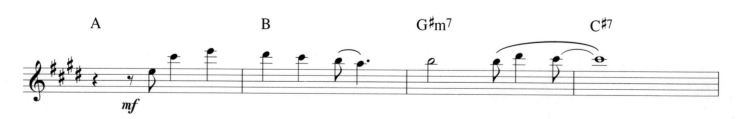

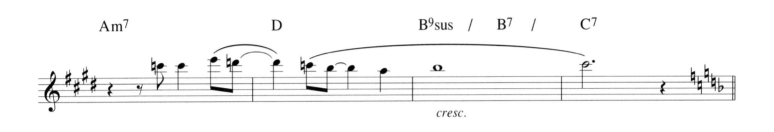

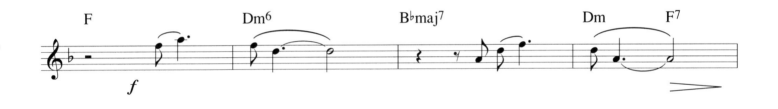

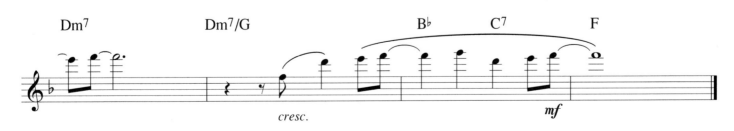

DON'T CRY FOR ME ARGENTINA

Andrew Lloyd Webber

✱ Also try these notes up the octave for practice.

SECTION 10 (BOOK TWO, LESSONS 13-15)

Range of notes:

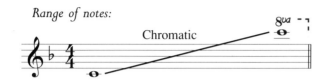

Objectives:

1. More chromatic writing and enharmonic notation.

2. Mixing ♪ and ♪♪ groups.

PENNY LANE

John Lennon & Paul McCartney

© Copyright 1967 Northern Songs, under licence to EMI Songs Limited, 127 Charing Cross Road, London WC2.

All Rights Reserved. International Copyright Secured.

BIG SPENDER

Cy Coleman